"...LET SLIP THE DOGS OF WAR!"

BY

Murray Ball.

GRRR...RRRRR

ORIN BOOKS

OBSEQUIOUSNESS
HUMILITY
NON-THREATENING
...SUBMISSION...

SLITHER SLITHER SLIDE GROVEL

3

"Cry havoc . . .

. . . and let slip the dogs of war!"

7

© 1988 Diogenes Designs Ltd

14

15

17

19

24

25

26

33

45

© 1988 Diogenes Designs Ltd

FF 3275

47

© 1988 Diogenes Designs Ltd

51

53

56

58

© 1988 Diogenes Designs Ltd.

© 1988 Diogenes Designs Ltd

Murray Ball.

FF3331

WAL' IS PLAYING GOAL DEFENCE FOR CHEEKY HOBSON'S MERCANTILE NETBALL TEAM...

© 1988 Diogenes Designs Ltd

HE WAS A BIT WORRIED THAT HE WOULD BE THE ONLY BLOKE AT THE TOURNAMENT...

..BUT MURU O'REGAN IS PLAYIN' GOAL SHOOTER FOR JOSELYN'S LADIESWEAR.

FF 3332

FUNNILY ENOUGH THEY ARE BOTH IN THE FRONT ROW OF THEIR RUGBY TEAMS...

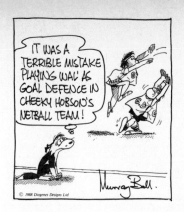

79

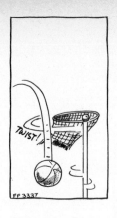

© 1988 Diogenes Designs Ltd

© 1988 Diogenes Designs Ltd   PP 3340

89

93

© 1988 Diogenes Designs Ltd

© 1988 Diogenes Designs Ltd   FF 3393

99

© 1988 Diogenes Designs Ltd

© 1988 Diogenes Designs Ltd

© 1988 Diogenes Designs Ltd

FF 3449

THUMP!
THUMP!
THUMP!

© 1988 Diogenes Designs Ltd

113

120

122

© 1989 Diogenes Designs Ltd

133

© 1989 Diogenes Designs Ltd

© 1989 Diogenes Designs Ltd